Name _____

ASSETS = LIABILITIES + OWNER EQUITY

CASH	+	ACCOUNTS RECEIVABLE	+	PREPAID RENT	+	SUPPLIES	+	TOOLS	+	TRUCKS	=	ACCOUNTS PAYABLE	+	TED SHARP, CAPITAL

PROBLEM 1-2 or 1-2A

Name _____

EM 1/29/80

		Assets				= Liabilities +	Owner Equity
Date	Cash	Accounts Receivable	Prepaid Rent	Office Supplies	Law Library	Accounts Payable	Jane Lee, Capital
Oct 1	+1,500				+1,000		+2,500
11/1	-900		+900				2,500
	600		900		1,000		2,500
11/2	-65			+65			
	535		900	165	1,000		2,500
11/5	535				+750	#150	2,500
	+50				1,750	-#150	+50
	585		900	65	1,750		2,550
11/8	585	+350	900	65	1,750	150	+350
	-250	350	900	65	1,750	150	2,900
	335	350	900	65	1,750	150	-250
11/14	-50	350	900	65	1,750	150	2,650
	285	350	900	65	1,750	150	2,650
11/15	285	+400	900	65	1,750	150	2,650
	+200	750	900	65	1,750	-50	+400
	485	-200	900	65	1,750	100	3,050
11/15	-20	550	900	65	1,750	100	3,650
	465	550	900	65	1,750	100	-20
11/20	-250	550	900	65	1,750	100	3,030
	215	550	900	-15	1,750	100	3,250
11/24	215	550	900	50	1,150	100	2,780
11/31	215	550	-300	50	1,150	100	27.15
11/31		550	600		1,150	100	2,765
11/31							300
11/31							2,465

Jane Lee, Attorney
Balance Sheet, October 31, 19

ASSETS			LIABILITIES		
CASH	$	2150 00			
OFFICE SUPPLIES		50 00	ACCOUNT PAYABLE	$	100 00
ACCOUNT RECEIVABLE		550 00			
PREPAID RENT		600 00			
LAW LIB.		1150 00	OWNER EQUITY		
TOTAL ASSETS	$	2565 00	JANE LEE, CAPITAL		2465 00
			TOTAL EQUITIES	$	2565 00

Jane Lee, Attorney
Income Statement for October

REVENUES:			
LEGAL FEES	$	800 00	$ 800 00
TOTAL REVENUES			
OPERATING EXPENSES			
SALARIES EXPENSE	#	500 00	
RENT EXPENSES		300 00	
TELEPHONE EXPENSES		20 00	
OFFICE EXPENSES		15 00	
TOTAL OPERATING EXPENSES			835 00
NET LOSS			# -35 00

balance sheet

DATE	ASSETS *resources of business*						= LIABILITIES *debts of business* +	OWNER EQUITY *claim*
	CASH	+ ACCOUNTS RECEIVABLE	+ PREPAID RENT	+ PREPAID INSURANCE	+ OFFICE SUPPLIES	+ LAW LIBRARY	= ACCOUNTS PAYABLE +	CARL HALL, CAPITAL
July 1	+2,000					+400		+2,400
"	-900		+900					
"	-25				+25			
"	-500					+2,000	+1,500	
July 5	-120			+120				
7	+50							+50 Rev.
10		+1,000			+40		+400	600 Rev.
13						+200	+200	
15	-300							-300 Exp
17	-40	+400					-40	+400 Rev
18		-600						
20	+600	+350						+350 Rev
22		-400						
27	+400							
31	-25							-25 exp
31	-20							-20 exp
31	-300		-300					-300 exp
31				-10				-300 exp
31					-15			-10
31								-15
	$820	$350	$600	$110	$56	$2,600	$2,600 = 1700	2830
							4530 = 4530	

CARL HALL, ATTORNEY
BALANCE SHEET JULY 31, 1980

ASSETS		LIABILITIES	
CASH	820	ACCOUNT PAYABLE	1700
ACCOUNT REC	350		
PREPAID RENT	600		
PREPAID INS.	110		
OFFICE SUPPLIES	50		
LAW LIB	2600		
		OWNER EQUITY	
TOTAL ASSETS	4530	CARL HALL, CAPITAL	2830
		TOTAL LIBS CAP	4530 00

CARL HALL, ATTORNEY

REVENUES		
LEGAL FEES		1400 00
OP EXPENSES		
SAL. EXP	600 00	
OFFICE EXP	1500	
RENT EXP	300 00	
INSURANCE	1600	
TELEPHONE	20 00	
UTILITIES	20 00	
		-970 00
NET INCOME		430 00

Cash

Truck

Accounts Payable

Accounts Receivable

Dale Sims, Capital

Repair Supplies

Dale Sims, Withdrawals

Prepaid Rent

Revenue from Repairs

Office Equipment

Advertising Expense

Tools

Utilities Expense

GENERAL JOURNAL
                                                                PAGE 1

DATE	ACCOUNT TITLES AND EXPLANATION	FO-LIO	DEBIT	CREDIT

DATE	ACCOUNT TITLES AND EXPLANATION	Fo-LIO	DEBIT	CREDIT

GENERAL LEDGER

Cash   ACCT. NO. 1

DATE		EXPLANATION	FO-LIO	DEBIT	CREDIT	BALANCE

Accounts Receivable   ACCT. NO. 2

DATE		EXPLANATION	FO-LIO	DEBIT	CREDIT	BALANCE

Prepaid Rent   ACCT. NO. 3

DATE		EXPLANATION	FO-LIO	DEBIT	CREDIT	BALANCE

Prepaid Insurance   ACCT. NO. 4

DATE		EXPLANATION	FO-LIO	DEBIT	CREDIT	BALANCE

Office Supplies   Acct. No. 5

DATE		EXPLANATION	FO-LIO	DEBIT	CREDIT	BALANCE

Office Equipment   Acct. No. 6

DATE		EXPLANATION	FO-LIO	DEBIT	CREDIT	BALANCE

Accounts Payable   Acct. No. 7

DATE		EXPLANATION	FO-LIO	DEBIT	CREDIT	BALANCE

Jane Hall, Capital   Acct. No. 8

DATE		EXPLANATION	FO-LIO	DEBIT	CREDIT	BALANCE

Jane Hall, Withdrawals   Acct. No. 9

DATE		EXPLANATION	FO-LIO	DEBIT	CREDIT	BALANCE

Accounting Revenue   ACCT. No. 10

DATE		EXPLANATION	FO-LIO	DEBIT	CREDIT	BALANCE

Utilities Expense   ACCT. No. 11

DATE		EXPLANATION	FO-LIO	DEBIT	CREDIT	BALANCE

Cash

Building

Accounts Payable

Mortgage Payable

Accounts Receivable

Ted Darby, Capital

Office Supplies

Ted Darby, Withdrawals

Office Equipment

Commissions Earned

Automobile

Management Fees Earned

Land

Advertising Expense

Salaries Expense   *Telephone Expense*

GENERAL JOURNAL

DATE	ACCOUNT TITLES AND EXPLANATION	Fo-LIO	DEBIT	CREDIT

DATE	ACCOUNT TITLES AND EXPLANATION	FO-LIO	DEBIT	CREDIT

GENERAL LEDGER

Cash   ACCT. NO. 1

DATE		EXPLANATION	FO-LIO	DEBIT	CREDIT	BALANCE

Accounts Receivable   ACCT. NO. 2

DATE		EXPLANATION	FO-LIO	DEBIT	CREDIT	BALANCE

Prepaid Rent   ACCT. NO. 3

DATE		EXPLANATION	FO-LIO	DEBIT	CREDIT	BALANCE

Prepaid Insurance   ACCT. NO. 4

DATE		EXPLANATION	FO-LIO	DEBIT	CREDIT	BALANCE

Office Supplies   ACCT. NO. 5

DATE	EXPLANATION	FO-LIO	DEBIT	CREDIT	BALANCE

Office Equipment   ACCT. NO. 6

DATE	EXPLANATION	FO-LIO	DEBIT	CREDIT	BALANCE

Law Library   ACCT. NO. 7

DATE	EXPLANATION	FO-LIO	DEBIT	CREDIT	BALANCE

Notes Payable   ACCT. NO. 8

DATE	EXPLANATION	FO-LIO	DEBIT	CREDIT	BALANCE

Accounts Payable   ACCT. NO. 9

DATE	EXPLANATION	FO-LIO	DEBIT	CREDIT	BALANCE

Ann Howe, Capital   ACCT. No. 10

DATE	EXPLANATION	FO-LIO	DEBIT	CREDIT	BALANCE

Ann Howe, Withdrawals   ACCT. No. 11

DATE	EXPLANATION	FO-LIO	DEBIT	CREDIT	BALANCE

Legal Fees Earned   ACCT. No. 12

DATE	EXPLANATION	FO-LIO	DEBIT	CREDIT	BALANCE

Salaries Expense   ACCT. No. 13

DATE	EXPLANATION	FO-LIO	DEBIT	CREDIT	BALANCE

Utilities Expense   ACCT. No. 14

DATE	EXPLANATION	FO-LIO	DEBIT	CREDIT	BALANCE

DATE		EXPLANATION	FO-LIO	DEBIT	CREDIT	BALANCE

Interest Expense　　　　　ACCT. No. 15

Em 2/5/80

GENERAL JOURNAL   PAGE 1

DATE			ACCOUNT TITLES AND EXPLANATION	Fo-LIO	DEBIT	CREDIT
1980						
July		1	CASH	1	150000	
			Ann Evans, Capital	7		150000
		1	PREPAID RENT	3	80000	
			CASH	1		80000
		1	PREPAID INSURANCE	4	12000	
			CASH	1		12000
		2	DRAFTING SUPPLIES	5	3000	
			ACCOUNTS PAYABLE	6		3000
		8	CASH	1	25000	
			ARCHITECTURAL FEES EARN	9		25000
		15	ACCOUNT RECIEVABLE	2	45000	
			ARCHITECTURAL FEES EARNED	9		45000
		17	ACCOUNT PAYABLE	6	3000	
			CASH	1		3000
		22	ACCOUNTS RECIEVABLE	2	1500	
			ARCHITECTURAL FEES EARNED	9		1500
		25	CASH	1	45000	
			ACCOUNT RECIEVABLE	2		45000
		27	ANN EVANS, WITHDRAWALS	8	20000	
			CASH	1		20000
		29	DRAFTING SUPPLIES	5	4500	
			ACCOUNTS PAYABLE	6		4500
		31	BLUE PRINTING EXPENSE	11	7500	
			CASH	1		7500
		31	UTILITY EXPENSE	12	3500	
			CASH	1		3500
		31	RENT EXPENSE	10	40000	
			PREPAID RENT	3		4000

DATE 1980		ACCOUNT TITLES AND EXPLANATION	FO-LIO	DEBIT	CREDIT
July	31	INSURANCE EXPENSE	13	1100	
		PREPAID INSURANCE	4		1000
	31	DRAFTING SUPPLY EXPENSE	14	2500	
		DRAFTING SUPPLIES	5		2500

Cash   Acct. No. 1

DATE 1980		EXPLANATION	FO-LIO	DEBIT	CREDIT	BALANCE
July	1	INVESTMENT	9-1	150000		150000
	1	PREPAID RENT	9-1		80000	70000
	1	PREPAID INSURANCE	9-1		120	58000
	8	ARCHITECTURAL FEES	9-1	25000		83000
	15	DRAFTING SUPPLIES	9-1		3000	80000
	25	ARCHITECTURAL FEES	9-1	45000		125000
	27	ANN EVAN WITHDRAW	9-1		20000	105000
	31	BLUEPRINTING EXPENSE	9-1		7500	97500
	31	UTILITY EXPENSE	9-1		3500	94000

Accounts Receivable   Acct. No. 2

DATE 1980		EXPLANATION	FO-LIO	DEBIT	CREDIT	BALANCE
July	15	TAHOE CONSTRUCTION	9-1	45000		45000
	22	LAKE REALTY	9-1	15000		60000
	25	TAHOE CONSTRUCTION	9-1		45000	15000

Prepaid Rent   Acct. No. 3

DATE 1980		EXPLANATION	FO-LIO	DEBIT	CREDIT	BALANCE
July	1	TWO MONTHS RENT	9-1	80000		80000
					40000	40000

Prepaid Insurance   Acct. No. 4

DATE 1980		EXPLANATION	FO-LIO	DEBIT	CREDIT	BALANCE
July	1	1 YEAR'S PROTECTION	9-1	12000		12000
	31	1 month's expense	9-2		1000	11000

Drafting Supplies   ACCT. NO. 5

DATE	EXPLANATION	FO-LIO	DEBIT	CREDIT	BALANCE
1980					
July 2		G-1	3000		3000
29		G-1	4500		7500
31	EXPENSE	G-2		2500	5000

Accounts Payable   ACCT. NO. 6

DATE	EXPLANATION	FO-LIO	DEBIT	CREDIT	BALANCE
1980					
July 2	DRAFTING SUPPLYS	G-1		3000	3000
15	" "	G-1	3000		—
29	" "	G-1		4500	4500

Ann Evans, Capital   ACCT. NO. 7

DATE	EXPLANATION	FO-LIO	DEBIT	CREDIT	BALANCE
1980					
July 1	INVESTMENTS	G-1		150000	150000

Ann Evans, Withdrawals   ACCT. NO. 8

DATE	EXPLANATION	FO-LIO	DEBIT	CREDIT	BALANCE
1980					
July 27	PERSONAL EXPENSES	G-1	20000		20000

Architectural Fees Earned   ACCT. NO. 9

DATE	EXPLANATION	FO-LIO	DEBIT	CREDIT	BALANCE
1980					
July 8	CONTRACTOR	G-1		25000	25000
15	TAHOE CONSTRUCTION	G-1		45000	70000
22	LAKE REALTY	G-1		15000	85000

Rent Expense   ACCT. No. 10

DATE	EXPLANATION	FO-LIO	DEBIT	CREDIT	BALANCE
1980					
July 31		9-1	400 00		400 00

Blueprinting Expense   ACCT. No. 11

DATE	EXPLANATION	FO-LIO	DEBIT	CREDIT	BALANCE
1980					
July 31		9-1	75 00		75 00

Utilities Expense   ACCT. No. 12

DATE	EXPLANATION	FO-LIO	DEBIT	CREDIT	BALANCE
1980					
July 31		9-1	35 00		35 00

Insurance Expense   ACCT. No. 13

DATE	EXPLANATION	FO-LIO	DEBIT	CREDIT	BALANCE
1980					
July 31		9-2	10 00		10 00

Drafting Supplies Expense   ACCT. No. 14

DATE	EXPLANATION	FO-LIO	DEBIT	CREDIT	BALANCE
1980					
July 31		9-2	25 00		25 00

ANN EVANS, Architect
TRIAL BALANCE, JULY 31, 1980

	Debit	Credit
CASH	$9400 00	
PREPAID RENT	4000 00	
ACCOUNTS RECEIVABLE	1500 00	
PREPAID INSURANCE	1100 00	
DRAFTING SUPPLIES	500 00	
ACCOUNTS PAYABLE		$450 00
ANN EVANS, CAPITAL		15000 00
ANN EVANS, WITHDRAWALS	2000 00	
ARCHITECTURAL FEES EARNED		8500 00
RENT EXPENSES	400 00	
BLUEPRINTING EXPENSE	7500	
UTILITIES EXPENSE	3500	
INSURANCE EXPENSE	1000	
DRAFTING SUPPLIES EXPENSE	2500	
TOTALS	$23950 0	$23950 0

ANN EVANS, ARCHITECT
BALANCE SHEET, JULY 31, 1980

ASSETS		LIABILITIES	
CASH	$94000	ACCOUNTS PAYABLE	$4500
ACCOUNT RECIEVABLE	15000		
PREPAID RENT	40000		
PREPAID INSURANCE	11000	OWNER EQUITY	
DRAFTING SUPPLIES	5000	ANN EVANS, CAPITAL	160500
TOTAL ASSETS	$165000	TOTAL EQUITIES	165000

ANN EVANS, ARCHITECT
INCOME STATEMENT FOR JULY

REVENUES				
ARCHITECTURAL FEES EARNED	$85000			
TOTAL REVENUES				$85000
OPERATING EXPENSES				
RENT EXPENSES	$4400			
BLUE PRINTING EXPENSES	75			
UTILITIES EXPENSES	35			
INSURANCE EXPENSES	10			
DRAFTING SUPPLY EXPENSES	25			
				54500
				$30500

GENERAL JOURNAL   PAGE 1

DATE	ACCOUNT TITLES AND EXPLANATION	Fo-LIO	DEBIT	CREDIT

DATE	ACCOUNT TITLES AND EXPLANATION	FO-LIO	DEBIT	CREDIT

GENERAL LEDGER

Cash   ACCT. NO. 1

DATE		EXPLANATION	FO-LIO	DEBIT	CREDIT	BALANCE
Dec.	31	Balance	✔			3 1 4 5 00

Accounts Receivable   ACCT. NO. 2

DATE		EXPLANATION	FO-LIO	DEBIT	CREDIT	BALANCE

Prepaid Insurance   ACCT. NO. 3

DATE		EXPLANATION	FO-LIO	DEBIT	CREDIT	BALANCE
Dec.	31	Balance	✔			3 8 0 00

Office Supplies   ACCT. NO. 4

DATE		EXPLANATION	FO-LIO	DEBIT	CREDIT	BALANCE
Dec.	31	Balance	✔			3 3 5 00

Office Equipment   ACCT. NO. 5

DATE		EXPLANATION	FO-LIO	DEBIT	CREDIT	BALANCE
Dec.	31	Balance	✔			2 9 7 5 00

Accumulated Depreciation, Office Equipment   ACCT. NO. 6

DATE	EXPLANATION	FO-LIO	DEBIT	CREDIT	BALANCE
Dec. 31	Balance	✔			6 1 5 00

Automobile   ACCT. NO. 7

DATE	EXPLANATION	FO-LIO	DEBIT	CREDIT	BALANCE
Dec. 31	Balance	✔			3 6 4 5 00

Accumulated Depreciation, Automobile   ACCT. NO. 8

DATE	EXPLANATION	FO-LIO	DEBIT	CREDIT	BALANCE
Dec. 31	Balance	✔			1 1 5 0 00

Accounts Payable   ACCT. NO. 9

DATE	EXPLANATION	FO-LIO	DEBIT	CREDIT	BALANCE
Dec. 31	Balance	✔			7 5 00

Office Salaries Payable   ACCT. NO. 10

DATE	EXPLANATION	FO-LIO	DEBIT	CREDIT	BALANCE

Unearned Management Fees   ACCT. NO. 11

DATE	EXPLANATION	FO-LIO	DEBIT	CREDIT	BALANCE
Dec. 31	Balance	✔			4 5 0 00

Marie Sloan, Capital — Acct. No. 12

DATE		EXPLANATION	FO-LIO	DEBIT	CREDIT	BALANCE
Dec.	31	Balance	✔			6 1 4 0 00

Marie Sloan, Withdrawals — Acct. No. 13

DATE		EXPLANATION	FO-LIO	DEBIT	CREDIT	BALANCE
Dec.	31	Balance	✔			9 0 0 0 00

Sales Commissions Earned — Acct. No. 14

DATE		EXPLANATION	FO-LIO	DEBIT	CREDIT	BALANCE
Dec.	31	Balance	✔			17 4 6 0 00

Management Fees Earned — Acct. No. 15

DATE		EXPLANATION	FO-LIO	DEBIT	CREDIT	BALANCE

Office Salaries Expense — Acct. No. 16

DATE		EXPLANATION	FO-LIO	DEBIT	CREDIT	BALANCE
Dec.	31	Balance	✔			4 5 0 0 00

Advertising Expense — Acct. No. 17

DATE		EXPLANATION	FO-LIO	DEBIT	CREDIT	BALANCE
Dec.	31	Balance	✔			5 6 5 00

Rent Expense   Acct. No. 18

DATE	EXPLANATION	FO-LIO	DEBIT	CREDIT	BALANCE
Dec. 31	Balance	✓			1 2 0 0 00

Telephone Expense   Acct. No. 19

DATE	EXPLANATION	FO-LIO	DEBIT	CREDIT	BALANCE
Dec. 31	Balance	✓			1 4 5 00

Insurance Expense   Acct. No. 20

DATE	EXPLANATION	FO-LIO	DEBIT	CREDIT	BALANCE

Office Supplies Expense   Acct. No. 21

DATE	EXPLANATION	FO-LIO	DEBIT	CREDIT	BALANCE

Depreciation Expense, Office Equipment   Acct. No. 22

DATE	EXPLANATION	FO-LIO	DEBIT	CREDIT	BALANCE

Depreciation Expense, Automobile   Acct. No. 23

DATE	EXPLANATION	FO-LIO	DEBIT	CREDIT	BALANCE

GENERAL JOURNAL   PAGE 1

DATE	ACCOUNT TITLES AND EXPLANATION	FO-LIO	DEBIT	CREDIT	

CHAPTER 3   PROBLEM 3-2 or 3-2A (Concluded)

all 3-3
of
2/12/80 em

GENERAL LEDGER

Cash   ACCT. NO. 1

DATE		EXPLANATION	FO-LIO	DEBIT	CREDIT	BALANCE
Dec. 31		Balance	✔			2460 00

Accounts Receivable   ACCT. NO. 2

DATE		EXPLANATION	FO-LIO	DEBIT	CREDIT	BALANCE
1980 Dec. 31		Balance	✔			680 00
Dec. 31			g-2	14000		820 00

Prepaid Insurance   ACCT. NO. 3

DATE		EXPLANATION	FO-LIO	DEBIT	CREDIT	BALANCE
1980 Dec. 31		Balance	✔			1340 00
	31		g-1		91500	425 00

Office Supplies   ACCT. NO. 4

DATE		EXPLANATION	FO-LIO	DEBIT	CREDIT	BALANCE
Dec. 31		Balance	✔			210 00
	31		g-1		155	5500

Office Equipment   ACCT. NO. 5

DATE		EXPLANATION	FO-LIO	DEBIT	CREDIT	BALANCE
Dec. 31		Balance	✔			1540 00

Accumulated Depreciation, Office Equipment   ACCT. NO. 6

DATE		EXPLANATION	FO-LIO	DEBIT	CREDIT	BALANCE
Dec. 31		Balance	✔			320 00
	31		g-1		130	450 00

Trucks   ACCT. No. 7

DATE		EXPLANATION	FO-LIO	DEBIT	CREDIT	BALANCE
Dec.	31	Balance	✔			13 8 0 0 00

Accumulated Depreciation, Trucks   ACCT. No. 8

DATE		EXPLANATION	FO-LIO	DEBIT	CREDIT	BALANCE
Dec.	31	Balance	✔			2 6 3 0 00
Dec 31			g-1		287 50	5 5 05

Buildings   ACCT. No. 9

DATE		EXPLANATION	FO-LIO	DEBIT	CREDIT	BALANCE
Dec.	31	Balance	✔			38 3 0 0 00

Accumulated Depreciation, Buildings   ACCT. No. 10

DATE		EXPLANATION	FO-LIO	DEBIT	CREDIT	BALANCE
Dec.	31	Balance	✔			10 9 0 0 00
	31		g-1		21 0 00	13 0 00

Land   ACCT. No. 11

DATE		EXPLANATION	FO-LIO	DEBIT	CREDIT	BALANCE
Dec.	31	Balance	✔			8 0 0 0 00

Accounts Payable   ACCT. No. 12

DATE		EXPLANATION	FO-LIO	DEBIT	CREDIT	BALANCE
Dec.	31	Balance	✔			8 7 5 00

Unearned Storage Fees   Acct. No. 13

DATE		EXPLANATION	FO-LIO	DEBIT	CREDIT	BALANCE
Dec. 31		Balance	✔			6 8 5 00
	31		g-1	385 00		300 00

Wages Payable   Acct. No. 14

DATE	EXPLANATION	FO-LIO	DEBIT	CREDIT	BALANCE
19__ Dec 31		g-2		285 00	285 00

Mortgage Payable   Acct. No. 15

DATE		EXPLANATION	FO-LIO	DEBIT	CREDIT	BALANCE
Dec. 31		Balance	✔			20 0 0 0 00

Ted Davis, Capital   Acct. No. 16

DATE		EXPLANATION	FO-LIO	DEBIT	CREDIT	BALANCE
Dec. 31		Balance	✔			18 4 9 0 00

Ted Davis, Withdrawals   Acct. No. 17

DATE		EXPLANATION	FO-LIO	DEBIT	CREDIT	BALANCE
Dec. 31		Balance	✔			8 4 0 0 00

Revenue from Moving Services   Acct. No. 18

DATE		EXPLANATION	FO-LIO	DEBIT	CREDIT	BALANCE
Dec. 31		Balance	✔			42 9 9 5 00

Storage Fees Earned
ACCT. No. 19

DATE		EXPLANATION	FO-LIO	DEBIT	CREDIT	BALANCE
Dec.	31	Balance	✔			2 9 6 0 00
	31		g-1		3 8 5 00	3 3 4 5 00
			g-2		1 4 0 00	3 4 8 5 00

Office Salaries Expense
ACCT. No. 20

DATE		EXPLANATION	FO-LIO	DEBIT	CREDIT	BALANCE
Dec.	31	Balance	✔			5 2 0 0 00

Truck Drivers' Wages
ACCT. No. 21

DATE		EXPLANATION	FO-LIO	DEBIT	CREDIT	BALANCE
Dec.	31	Balance	✔			18 4 1 0 00
	31		g-2	2 8 5		8 6 9 5 00

Gas, Oil, and Repairs
ACCT. No. 22

DATE		EXPLANATION	FO-LIO	DEBIT	CREDIT	BALANCE
Dec.	31	Balance	✔			1 5 1 5 00

Insurance Expense
ACCT. No. 23

DATE		EXPLANATION	FO-LIO	DEBIT	CREDIT	BALANCE
1940						
Dec. 31			g-1	9 1 5 00		9 1 5

Office Supplies Expense
ACCT. No. 24

DATE		EXPLANATION	FO-LIO	DEBIT	CREDIT	BALANCE
1940						
Dec. 31			g-1	1 5 5 00		1 5 5 00

Depreciation Expense, Office Equipment   Acct. No. 25

DATE		EXPLANATION	FO-LIO	DEBIT	CREDIT	BALANCE
1980						
Dec	31		g1	13600		13600

Depreciation Expense, Trucks   Acct. No. 26

DATE		EXPLANATION	FO-LIO	DEBIT	CREDIT	BALANCE
1980						
Dec	3		g-1	207500		287500

Depreciation Expense, Buildings   Acct. No. 27

DATE		EXPLANATION	FO-LIO	DEBIT	CREDIT	BALANCE
1980						
Dec	31		g-1	210000		210000

GENERAL JOURNAL   PAGE 1

DATE		ACCOUNT TITLES AND EXPLANATION	FO-LIO	DEBIT	CREDIT
1980					
Dec	31	Insurance Expense	23	91500	
		Prepaid Insurance	3		91500
	31	Office Supplies Expense	24	15500	
		Office Supplies	4		15500
	31	Depreciation Expense, Office Equipment	25	13000	
		Accumulated Depreciation,			
		Office Equipment	6		13000
	31	Depreciation Expense, Trucks	26	287500	
		Accumulated Depreciation,			
		Trucks	8		287500
	31	Depreciation Expense, Buildings	27	21000	
		Accumulated Depreciation,			
		Buildings	10		210000
	31	Unearned Storage Fees	13	385	
		Storage Fees Earned	19		38500

DATE		ACCOUNT TITLES AND EXPLANATION	FO-LIO	DEBIT	CREDIT
1980					
Dec	31	Accounts Recievable	2	14000	
		STORAGE FEES EARNED	9		14000
	31	TRUCK DRIVERS WAGES	21	28500	
		WAGES PAYABLE	14		28500

CHEVRON MOVING AND STORAGE COMPANY
ADJUSTED TRIAL BALANCE, DECEMBER 31, 1980

CASH	$2460 00	
ACCOUNTS RECIEVABLE	820 00	
PREPAID INSURANCE	425 00	
OFFICE SUPPLIES	55 00	
OFFICE EQUIPTMENT	1540 00	
ACCUMLATED DEPRECIATION, OFFICE EQUIPTMENT		$ 450 00
TRUCKS	13800 00	
ACCUMLATED DEPRECIATION, TRUCKS		5055
BUILDINGS	38360 00	
ACUMULATED DEPRECIATION, BUILDINGS		130 00
LAND	8060 00	
ACCOUNTS PAYABLE		875 00
UNEARNED STORAGE FEES		300 00
MORTGAGE PAYABLE		20000 00
TED DAVIS' CAPITAL		18490 00
TED DAVIS' WITHDRAWALS	2400 00	
REVENUE FROM MOVING SERVICES		42995 00
STORAGE FEES EARNED		2485 00
OFFICE SALARIES EXPENSES	5200 00	
TRUCK DRIVERS' WAGES EXPENSE	18695 00	
GAS, OIL, AND REPAIRS EXPETSE	1515 00	
INSURANCE EXPENSE	915 00	
OFFICE SUPPLIES EXPETSE	155 00	
DEPRECIATED EXPENSE, OFFICE EQUIPMENT	130 00	
DEPRECIATED EXPENSE, TRUCKS	2875 00	
DEPRECIATED EXPENSE, BUILDINGS	2100 00	
WAGES PAYABLE		285
TOTALS	$105385 00	$105385 00

CHEVRON MOVING AND STORAGE COMPANY
INCOME STATEMENT FOR MONTH ENDING DECEMBER 31,

REVENUE:				
MOVING SERVICES		42995	$42995	00
STORAGE FEES EARNED			3485	00
TOTAL REVENUE			$46480	00
OPERATING EXPENSES				
OFFICE SALARIES EXPENSE	$5200			
TRUCK DRIVERS WAGES EXPENSE	18695			
GAS OIL AND REPAIRS EXPENSE	1515			
INSURANCE EXPENSE	915			
OFFICE SUPPLIES EXPENSE	155			
DEPRECIATION EXPENSE, OFFICE EQUIPMENT	130			
DEPRECIATION EXPENSE, TRUCKS	2875			
DEPRECIATION EXPENSE, BUILDINGS	2100			
TOTAL OPERATING EXPENSES			31585	00
NET INCOME			$14895	00

CHEVRON MOVING AND STORAGE COMPANY
BALANCE SHEET, DECEMBER 31, 1980

ASSETS

CURRENT ASSETS:			
CASH		$2460.00	
ACCOUNTS RECIEVABLE		820.00	
PREPAID INSURANCE		425.00	
OFFICE SUPPLIES		55.00	
TOTAL CURRENT ASSETS			$3760.00
PLANT AND EQUIPMENT:			
OFFICE EQUIPMENT	$1540.00		
LESS ACCUMULATED DEPRECIATION	-450.00		
TOTAL OFFICE EQUIPMENT		1090.00	
TRUCKS	$13800.00		
LESS ACCUMULATED DEPRECIATION	5655.00		
TOTAL TRUCK VALUE		8295.00	
BUILDINGS	$38300.00		
LESS ACCUMULATED DEPRECIATION	-13000.00		
TOTAL BUILDING VALUE		25300.00	
LAND		8000	
TOTAL PLANT AND EQUIPMENT			42685.00
			$46445.00

LIABILITIES

CURRENT LIABILITIES:			
ACCOUNTS PAYABLE		$875.00	
UNEARNED STORAGE FEES		360.00	
MORTAGE PAYABLE		20000.00	
WAGES PAYABLE		285.00	
TOTAL LIABILITIES			$21460.00
OWNER EQUITY			
TED DAVIS CAPITAL DEC. 1, 1980		18490	
DECEMBER NET INCOME	$1489.5		
LESS WITH DRAWALS	840.0		
EXCESS OF INCOME OVER WITHDRAWALS		1649500	
TED DAVIS CAPITAL DEC 31, 1980			24985.00
			$46445.00

GENERAL JOURNAL

DATE	ACCOUNT TITLES AND EXPLANATION	FO-LIO	DEBIT	CREDIT

DATE	ACCOUNT TITLES AND EXPLANATION	Fo-LIO	DEBIT	CREDIT

GENERAL LEDGER

Cash   ACCT. NO. 1

DATE		EXPLANATION	FO-LIO	DEBIT	CREDIT	BALANCE
Dec.	31	Balance	✔			2 5 9 0 00

Accounts Receivable   ACCT. NO. 2

DATE		EXPLANATION	FO-LIO	DEBIT	CREDIT	BALANCE

Prepaid Insurance   ACCT. NO. 3

DATE		EXPLANATION	FO-LIO	DEBIT	CREDIT	BALANCE
Dec.	31	Balance	✔			6 1 5 00

Office Supplies   ACCT. NO. 4

DATE		EXPLANATION	FO-LIO	DEBIT	CREDIT	BALANCE
Dec.	31	Balance	✔			1 2 5 00

Office Equipment   ACCT. NO. 5

DATE		EXPLANATION	FO-LIO	DEBIT	CREDIT	BALANCE
Dec.	31	Balance	✔			1 2 5 0 00

Accumulated Depreciation, Office Equipment   ACCT. NO. 6

DATE		EXPLANATION	FO-LIO	DEBIT	CREDIT	BALANCE
Dec.	31	Balance	✔			3 2 5 00

Buildings and Improvements

ACCT. NO. 7

DATE		EXPLANATION	FO-LIO	DEBIT	CREDIT	BALANCE
Dec.	31	Balance	✔			65 0 0 0 00

Accumulated Depreciation, Buildings and Improvements

ACCT. NO. 8

DATE		EXPLANATION	FO-LIO	DEBIT	CREDIT	BALANCE
Dec.	31	Balance	✔			7 2 0 0 00

Land

ACCT. NO. 9

DATE		EXPLANATION	FO-LIO	DEBIT	CREDIT	BALANCE
Dec.	31	Balance	✔			90 0 0 0 00

Accounts Payable

ACCT. NO. 10

DATE		EXPLANATION	FO-LIO	DEBIT	CREDIT	BALANCE
Dec.	31	Balance	✔			2 1 5 00

Unearned Rent

ACCT. NO. 11

DATE		EXPLANATION	FO-LIO	DEBIT	CREDIT	BALANCE
Dec.	31	Balance	✔			5 0 0 00

Wages Payable

ACCT. NO. 12

DATE		EXPLANATION	FO-LIO	DEBIT	CREDIT	BALANCE

Property Taxes Payable — ACCT. NO. 13

DATE	EXPLANATION	FO-LIO	DEBIT	CREDIT	BALANCE

Interest Payable — ACCT. NO. 14

DATE	EXPLANATION	FO-LIO	DEBIT	CREDIT	BALANCE

Mortgage Payable — ACCT. NO. 15

DATE	EXPLANATION	FO-LIO	DEBIT	CREDIT	BALANCE
Dec. 31	Balance	✔			120 0 0 0 00

Margaret Martin, Capital — ACCT. NO. 16

DATE	EXPLANATION	FO-LIO	DEBIT	CREDIT	BALANCE
Dec. 31	Balance	✔			24 0 7 0 00

Margaret Martin, Withdrawals — ACCT. NO. 17

DATE	EXPLANATION	FO-LIO	DEBIT	CREDIT	BALANCE
Dec. 31	Balance	✔			12 0 0 0 00

Rent Earned — ACCT. NO. 18

DATE	EXPLANATION	FO-LIO	DEBIT	CREDIT	BALANCE
Dec. 31	Balance	✔			33 3 5 0 00

Wages Expense　　　　Acct. No. 19

DATE		EXPLANATION	FO-LIO	DEBIT	CREDIT	BALANCE
Dec. 31		Balance	✔			5 1 2 0 00

Utilities Expense　　　　Acct. No. 20

DATE		EXPLANATION	FO-LIO	DEBIT	CREDIT	BALANCE
Dec. 31		Balance	✔			3 4 0 00

Telephone Expense　　　　Acct: No. 21

DATE		EXPLANATION	FO-LIO	DEBIT	CREDIT	BALANCE
Dec. 31		Balance	✔			1 8 0 00

Property Taxes Expense　　　　Acct. No. 22

DATE		EXPLANATION	FO-LIO	DEBIT	CREDIT	BALANCE
Dec. 31		Balance	✔			1 8 4 0 00

Interest Expense　　　　Acct. No. 23

DATE		EXPLANATION	FO-LIO	DEBIT	CREDIT	BALANCE
Dec. 31		Balance	✔			6 6 0 0 00

Insurance Expense　　　　Acct. No. 24

DATE		EXPLANATION	FO-LIO	DEBIT	CREDIT	BALANCE

Office Supplies Expense   ACCT. NO. 25

DATE		EXPLANATION	FO-LIO	DEBIT	CREDIT	BALANCE

Depreciation Expense, Office Equipment   ACCT. NO. 26

DATE		EXPLANATION	FO-LIO	DEBIT	CREDIT	BALANCE

Depreciation Expense, Buildings and Improvements   ACCT. NO. 27

DATE		EXPLANATION	FO-LIO	DEBIT	CREDIT	BALANCE

(The work sheet for this problem is on page 257.)

GENERAL JOURNAL   PAGE 1

DATE	ACCOUNT TITLES AND EXPLANATION	FO-LIO	DEBIT	CREDIT

DATE	ACCOUNT TITLES AND EXPLANATION	FO-LIO	DEBIT	CREDIT

(The work sheet for this problem is on page 259.)

GENERAL JOURNAL

PAGE 1

DATE	ACCOUNT TITLES AND EXPLANATION	FO-LIO	DEBIT	CREDIT

DATE	ACCOUNT TITLES AND EXPLANATION	FO-LIO	DEBIT	CREDIT

GENERAL JOURNAL   PAGE 1

DATE	ACCOUNT TITLES AND EXPLANATION	FO-LIO	DEBIT	CREDIT

DATE	ACCOUNT TITLES AND EXPLANATION	Fo-LIO	DEBIT	CREDIT

DATE	ACCOUNT TITLES AND EXPLANATION	FO-LIO	DEBIT	CREDIT

DATE		ACCOUNT TITLES AND EXPLANATION	Fo-LIO	DEBIT	CREDIT

GENERAL LEDGER

Cash   ACCT. NO. 1

DATE		EXPLANATION	FO-LIO	DEBIT	CREDIT	BALANCE

Prepaid Insurance   ACCT. NO. 2

DATE		EXPLANATION	FO-LIO	DEBIT	CREDIT	BALANCE

Office Supplies   ACCT. NO. 3

DATE		EXPLANATION	FO-LIO	DEBIT	CREDIT	BALANCE

Automobile   ACCT. NO. 4

DATE		EXPLANATION	FO-LIO	DEBIT	CREDIT	BALANCE

Accumulated Depreciation, Automobile   ACCT. NO. 5

DATE		EXPLANATION	FO-LIO	DEBIT	CREDIT	BALANCE

Salaries Payable   ACCT. NO. 6

DATE		EXPLANATION	FO-LIO	DEBIT	CREDIT	BALANCE

Jane Reed, Capital   ACCT. NO. 7

DATE		EXPLANATION	FO-LIO	DEBIT	CREDIT	BALANCE

Jane Reed, Withdrawals   ACCT. NO. 8

DATE		EXPLANATION	FO-LIO	DEBIT	CREDIT	BALANCE

Income Summary   ACCT. NO. 9

DATE		EXPLANATION	FO-LIO	DEBIT	CREDIT	BALANCE

Commissions Earned   ACCT. No. 10

DATE	EXPLANATION	FO-LIO	DEBIT	CREDIT	BALANCE

Rent Expense   ACCT. No. 11

DATE	EXPLANATION	FO-LIO	DEBIT	CREDIT	BALANCE

Salaries Expense   ACCT. No. 12

DATE	EXPLANATION	FO-LIO	DEBIT	CREDIT	BALANCE

Gas, Oil, and Repairs Expense   ACCT. No. 13

DATE	EXPLANATION	FO-LIO	DEBIT	CREDIT	BALANCE

Telephone Expense   ACCT. No. 14

DATE	EXPLANATION	FO-LIO	DEBIT	CREDIT	BALANCE

Insurance Expense   ACCT. No. 15

DATE	EXPLANATION	FO-LIO	DEBIT	CREDIT	BALANCE

Office Supplies Expense   ACCT. No. 16

DATE	EXPLANATION	FO-LIO	DEBIT	CREDIT	BALANCE

Depreciation Expense, Automobile   ACCT. No. 17

DATE	EXPLANATION	FO-LIO	DEBIT	CREDIT	BALANCE

DESERT REALTY

Work Sheet for Month Ended June 30, 19____

ACCOUNT TITLES	TRIAL BALANCE		ADJUSTMENTS		ADJUSTED TRIAL BALANCE		INCOME STATEMENT		BALANCE SHEET	
	DR.	CR.	DR.	CR.	DR.	CR.	DR.	CR.	DR.	CR.

DESERT REALTY

Income Statement for Month Ended June 30, 19____

DESERT REALTY

Post-Closing Trial Balance, June 30, 19____

DESERT REALTY
Balance Sheet, June 30, 19____

DESERT REALTY

Work Sheet for Month Ended July 31, 19___

ACCOUNT TITLES	TRIAL BALANCE		ADJUSTMENTS		ADJUSTED TRIAL BALANCE		INCOME STATEMENT		BALANCE SHEET	
	DR.	CR.	DR.	CR.	DR.	CR.	DR.	CR.	DR.	CR.

DESERT REALTY

Income Statement for Month Ended July 31, 19____

DESERT REALTY

Post-Closing Trial Balance, July 31, 19____

DESERT REALTY
Balance Sheet, July 31, 19___

Cash   ACCT. No. 1

DATE	EXPLANATION	FO-LIO	DEBIT	CREDIT	BALANCE
Dec. 31	Balance	✔			2 7 7 5 00

Accounts Receivable   ACCT. No. 2

DATE	EXPLANATION	FO-LIO	DEBIT	CREDIT	BALANCE
Dec. 31	Balance	✔			4 5 5 00

Prepaid Insurance   ACCT. No. 3

DATE	EXPLANATION	FO-LIO	DEBIT	CREDIT	BALANCE
Dec. 31	Balance	✔			7 2 0 00

Office Supplies   ACCT. No. 4

DATE	EXPLANATION	FO-LIO	DEBIT	CREDIT	BALANCE
Dec. 31	Balance	✔			2 4 5 00

Office Equipment   ACCT. No. 5

DATE	EXPLANATION	FO-LIO	DEBIT	CREDIT	BALANCE
Dec. 31	Balance	✔			2 4 6 0 00

Accumulated Depreciation, Office Equipment ACCT. NO. 6

DATE	EXPLANATION	FO-LIO	DEBIT	CREDIT	BALANCE
Dec. 31	Balance	✔			4 7 0 00

Delivery Equipment ACCT. NO. 7

DATE	EXPLANATION	FO-LIO	DEBIT	CREDIT	BALANCE
Dec. 31	Balance	✔			10 7 9 0 00

Accumulated Depreciation, Delivery Equipment ACCT. NO. 8

DATE	EXPLANATION	FO-LIO	DEBIT	CREDIT	BALANCE
Dec. 31	Balance	✔			3 1 5 0 00

Accounts Payable ACCT. NO. 9

DATE	EXPLANATION	FO-LIO	DEBIT	CREDIT	BALANCE
Dec. 31	Balance	✔			2 9 0 00

Unearned Delivery Service Revenue ACCT. NO. 10

DATE	EXPLANATION	FO-LIO	DEBIT	CREDIT	BALANCE
Dec. 31	Balance	✔			4 5 0 00

Salaries and Wages Payable   ACCT. NO. 11

DATE	EXPLANATION	FO-LIO	DEBIT	CREDIT	BALANCE

Betty Lee, Capital   ACCT. NO. 12

DATE	EXPLANATION	FO-LIO	DEBIT	CREDIT	BALANCE
Dec. 31	Balance	✔			9 8 5 5 00

Betty Lee, Withdrawals   ACCT. NO. 13

DATE	EXPLANATION	FO-LIO	DEBIT	CREDIT	BALANCE
Dec. 31	Balance	✔			10 4 0 0 00

Income Summary   ACCT. NO. 14

DATE	EXPLANATION	FO-LIO	DEBIT	CREDIT	BALANCE

Delivery Service Revenue   ACCT. NO. 15

DATE	EXPLANATION	FO-LIO	DEBIT	CREDIT	BALANCE
Dec. 31	Balance	✔			38 9 3 5 00

Office Rent Expense   ACCT. NO. 16

DATE		EXPLANATION	FO-LIO	DEBIT	CREDIT	BALANCE
Dec.	31	Balance	✓			6 0 0 00

Telephone Expense   ACCT. NO. 17

DATE		EXPLANATION	FO-LIO	DEBIT	CREDIT	BALANCE
Dec.	31	Balance	✓			2 4 5 00

Office Salaries Expense   ACCT. NO. 18

DATE		EXPLANATION	FO-LIO	DEBIT	CREDIT	BALANCE
Dec.	31	Balance	✓			5 0 6 0 00

Insurance Expense, Office Equipment   ACCT. NO. 19

DATE		EXPLANATION	FO-LIO	DEBIT	CREDIT	BALANCE

Office Supplies Expense   ACCT. NO. 20

DATE		EXPLANATION	FO-LIO	DEBIT	CREDIT	BALANCE

Depreciation Expense, Office Equipment   ACCT. NO. 21

DATE	EXPLANATION	FO-LIO	DEBIT	CREDIT	BALANCE

Truck Drivers' Wages   ACCT. NO. 22

DATE	EXPLANATION	FO-LIO	DEBIT	CREDIT	BALANCE
Dec. 31	Balance	✔			16 3 2 0 00

Gas, Oil, and Repairs   ACCT. NO. 23

DATE	EXPLANATION	FO-LIO	DEBIT	CREDIT	BALANCE
Dec. 31	Balance	✔			2 1 8 0 00

Garage Rent Expense   ACCT. NO. 24

DATE	EXPLANATION	FO-LIO	DEBIT	CREDIT	BALANCE
Dec. 31	Balance	✔			9 0 0 00

Insurance Expense, Delivery Equipment   ACCT. NO. 25

DATE	EXPLANATION	FO-LIO	DEBIT	CREDIT	BALANCE

Depreciation Expense, Delivery Equipment — ACCT. NO. 26

DATE	EXPLANATION	FO-LIO	DEBIT	CREDIT	BALANCE

GENERAL JOURNAL — PAGE 1

DATE	ACCOUNT TITLES AND EXPLANATION	FO-LIO	DEBIT	CREDIT

DATE	ACCOUNT TITLES AND EXPLANATION	FO-LIO	DEBIT	CREDIT

VILLAGE DELIVERY SERVICE
Income Statement for Year Ended December 31, 19____

VILLAGE DELIVERY SERVICE
*Balance Sheet, December 31, 19*____

VILLAGE DELIVERY SERVICE
Post-Closing Trial Balance, December 31, 19____

GENERAL JOURNAL

DATE	ACCOUNT TITLES AND EXPLANATION	Fo-LIO	DEBIT	CREDIT

DATE	ACCOUNT TITLES AND EXPLANATION	FO-LIO	DEBIT	CREDIT

VARSITY SHOP
Work Sheet for Year Ended December 31, 19__

ACCOUNT TITLES	ADJUSTED TRIAL BALANCE DR.	ADJUSTED TRIAL BALANCE CR.	INCOME STATEMENT DR.	INCOME STATEMENT CR.	BALANCE SHEET DR.	BALANCE SHEET CR.
Cash	1 5 1 5 00					
Merchandise inventory	14 7 2 5 00					
Store supplies	1 5 0 00					
Office supplies	1 1 0 00					
Prepaid insurance	2 6 5 00					
Store equipment	10 1 4 0 00					
Accumulated depreciation, store equipment		2 2 1 0 00				
Office equipment	1 2 9 0 00					
Accumulated depreciation, office equipment		3 1 5 00				
Accounts payable		6 4 5 00				
Lois Bell, capital		19 7 9 5 00				
Lois Bell, withdrawals	10 2 0 0 00					
Sales		76 1 4 5 00				
Sales returns and allowances	9 4 5 00					
Purchases	39 1 1 0 00					
Purchases discounts		7 4 0 00				
Freight-in	8 3 5 00					
Sales salaries expense	7 9 6 0 00					
Rent expense, selling space	4 8 6 0 00					
Office salaries expense	5 2 0 0 00					
Rent expense, office space	5 4 0 00					
Insurance expense	4 8 5 00					
Store supplies expense	3 1 0 00					
Office supplies expense	1 1 5 00					
Depreciation expense, store equipment	10 1 5 00					
Depreciation expense, office equipment	2 1 0 00					
Salaries payable		1 3 0 00				
	99 9 8 0 00	99 9 8 0 00				

THE PRO SHOP

Work Sheet for Year Ended December 31, 19__

Account Titles	Trial Balance Dr.	Trial Balance Cr.	Adjustments Dr.	Adjustments Cr.	Adjusted Trial Balance Dr.	Adjusted Trial Balance Cr.	Income Statement Dr.	Income Statement Cr.	Balance Sheet Dr.	Balance Sheet Cr.
Cash	1,310 00				1,310 00					
Merchandise inventory	14,725 00				14,725 00					
Store supplies	650 00			(a)425 00	225 00					
Prepaid insurance	560 00			(b)415 00	145 00					
Store equipment	9,940 00				9,940 00					
Accum. depr., store equipment		2,780 00		(c)950 00		3,730 00				
Accounts payable		2,890 00				2,890 00				
Lee Dole, capital		17,550 00				17,550 00				
Lee Dole, withdrawals	9,225 00				9,225 00					
Sales		74,325 00				74,325 00				
Sales returns and allow.	525 00				525 00					
Sales discounts	1,390 00				1,390 00					
Purchases	39,880 00				39,880 00					
Purchases returns and allow.		315 00				315 00				
Purchases discounts		790 00				790 00				
Freight-in	1,125 00				1,125 00					
Sales salaries expense	12,215 00		(d)125 00		12,340 00					
Rent expense	6,000 00				6,000 00					
Advertising expense	465 00				465 00					
Utilities expense	640 00				640 00					
	98,650 00	98,650 00								
Store supplies expense			(a)425 00		425 00					
Insurance expense			(b)415 00		415 00					
Depr. expense, store equipment			(c)950 00		950 00					
Sales salaries payable				(d)125 00		125 00				
			1,915 00	1,915 00	99,725 00	99,725 00				

110

Merchandise Inventory   ACCT. No. 5

DATE	EXPLANATION	FO-LIO	DEBIT	CREDIT	BALANCE
Dec. 31		7	14 7 2 5 00		14 7 2 5 00

GENERAL JOURNAL   PAGE 14

DATE		ACCOUNT TITLES AND EXPLANATION	Fo-LIO	DEBIT	CREDIT

(The work sheet for this problem is on page 265.)

DATE	ACCOUNT TITLES AND EXPLANATION	FO-LIO	DEBIT	CREDIT

Merchandise Inventory   ACCT. NO. 115

DATE		EXPLANATION	FO-LIO	DEBIT	CREDIT	BALANCE
Dec.	31		6	14 6 6 5 00		14 6 6 5 00

PAGE 1

SALES JOURNAL

DATE	ACCOUNT DEBITED	INVOICE NUMBER	FO-LIO	AMOUNT

PAGE 1

PURCHASES JOURNAL

DATE	ACCOUNT CREDITED	DATE OF INVOICE	TERMS	FO-LIO	AMOUNT

CASH RECEIPTS JOURNAL

DATE	ACCOUNT CREDITED	EXPLANATION	FO-LIO	OTHER ACCOUNTS CREDIT	ACCOUNTS RECEIVABLE CREDIT	SALES CREDIT	SALES DISCOUNTS DEBIT	CASH DEBIT

CASH DISBURSEMENTS JOURNAL

DATE	CH. NO.	PAYEE	ACCOUNT DEBITED	FO-LIO	OTHER ACCOUNTS DEBIT	ACCOUNTS PAYABLE DEBIT	PURCHASES DISCOUNTS CREDIT	CASH CREDIT

GENERAL JOURNAL

PAGE 1

DATE	ACCOUNT TITLES AND EXPLANATION	FO-LIO	DEBIT	CREDIT

GENERAL LEDGER

Cash   ACCT. NO. 111

DATE	EXPLANATION	FO-LIO	DEBIT	CREDIT	BALANCE

Accounts Receivable   ACCT. NO. 113

DATE	EXPLANATION	FO-LIO	DEBIT	CREDIT	BALANCE

Store Equipment   ACCT. NO. 134

DATE		EXPLANATION	FO-LIO	DEBIT	CREDIT	BALANCE

Notes Payable   ACCT. NO. 211

DATE		EXPLANATION	FO-LIO	DEBIT	CREDIT	BALANCE

Accounts Payable   ACCT. NO. 212

DATE		EXPLANATION	FO-LIO	DEBIT	CREDIT	BALANCE

Sales   ACCT. NO. 411

DATE		EXPLANATION	FO-LIO	DEBIT	CREDIT	BALANCE

Sales Discounts   ACCT. NO. 412

DATE		EXPLANATION	FO-LIO	DEBIT	CREDIT	BALANCE

Purchases   ACCT. NO. 511

DATE	EXPLANATION	FO-LIO	DEBIT	CREDIT	BALANCE

Purchases Returns and Allowances   ACCT. NO. 512

DATE	EXPLANATION	FO-LIO	DEBIT	CREDIT	BALANCE

Purchases Discounts   ACCT. NO. 513

DATE	EXPLANATION	FO-LIO	DEBIT	CREDIT	BALANCE

Sales Salaries Expense   ACCT. NO. 615

DATE	EXPLANATION	FO-LIO	DEBIT	CREDIT	BALANCE

Rent Expense   ACCT. NO. 616

DATE	EXPLANATION	FO-LIO	DEBIT	CREDIT	BALANCE

NAME   *Carl Bates*   ACCOUNTS RECEIVABLE LEDGER

ADDRESS   *1412 West 24th Street*

DATE		EXPLANATION	FO-LIO	DEBIT	CREDIT	BALANCE

NAME   *Dale Hall*

ADDRESS   *4314 East Oak Avenue*

DATE		EXPLANATION	FO-LIO	DEBIT	CREDIT	BALANCE

NAME   *Walter Nash*

ADDRESS   *3434 West 18th Street*

DATE		EXPLANATION	FO-LIO	DEBIT	CREDIT	BALANCE

ACCOUNTS PAYABLE LEDGER

NAME   *Alpha Company*

ADDRESS   *Reno, Nevada*

DATE	EXPLANATION	FO-LIO	DEBIT	CREDIT	BALANCE

NAME   *Beta Company*

ADDRESS   *Carson City, Nevada*

DATE	EXPLANATION	FO-LIO	DEBIT	CREDIT	BALANCE

NAME   *Store Outfitters*

ADDRESS   *2112 West 23rd Street*

DATE	EXPLANATION	FO-LIO	DEBIT	CREDIT	BALANCE

NAME   *Western Company*

ADDRESS   *Reno, Nevada*

DATE	EXPLANATION	FO-LIO	DEBIT	CREDIT	BALANCE

SALES JOURNAL

PAGE 1

DATE	ACCOUNT DEBITED	INVOICE NUMBER	FO-LIO	AMOUNT

PURCHASES JOURNAL

PAGE 1

DATE	ACCOUNT CREDITED	DATE OF INVOICE	TERMS	FO-LIO	AMOUNT

CASH RECEIPTS JOURNAL

DATE	ACCOUNT CREDITED	EXPLANATION	FO-LIO	OTHER ACCOUNTS CREDIT	ACCOUNTS RECEIVABLE CREDIT	SALES CREDIT	SALES DISCOUNTS DEBIT	CASH DEBIT

CASH DISBURSEMENTS JOURNAL

DATE	CH. NO.	PAYEE	ACCOUNT DEBITED	FO-LIO	OTHER ACCOUNTS DEBIT	ACCOUNTS PAYABLE DEBIT	PURCHASES DISCOUNTS CREDIT	CASH CREDIT

GENERAL JOURNAL

DATE	ACCOUNT TITLES AND EXPLANATION	FO-LIO	DEBIT	CREDIT

ACCOUNTS RECEIVABLE LEDGER

NAME   *Fred Able*
ADDRESS   *1412 West 24th Street*

DATE	EXPLANATION	FO-LIO	DEBIT	CREDIT	BALANCE

NAME   *Tom Moss*
ADDRESS   *4314 East Oak Avenue*

DATE	EXPLANATION	FO-LIO	DEBIT	CREDIT	BALANCE

NAME   *John Rice*

ADDRESS   *3434 West 18th Street*

DATE		EXPLANATION	FO-LIO	DEBIT	CREDIT	BALANCE

ACCOUNTS PAYABLE LEDGER

NAME   *Case Company*

ADDRESS   *1212 Ninth Avenue*

DATE		EXPLANATION	FO-LIO	DEBIT	CREDIT	BALANCE

NAME   *New Company*

ADDRESS   *15th and Oak*

DATE		EXPLANATION	FO-LIO	DEBIT	CREDIT	BALANCE

NAME   *Office Equipment Company*

ADDRESS   *1412 East Maple Avenue*

DATE		EXPLANATION	FO-LIO	DEBIT	CREDIT	BALANCE

NAME   *Taylor Company*
ADDRESS   *32nd and Maple*

DATE	EXPLANATION	FO-LIO	DEBIT	CREDIT	BALANCE

GENERAL LEDGER

Cash   ACCT. NO. 111

DATE	EXPLANATION	FO-LIO	DEBIT	CREDIT	BALANCE

Accounts Receivable   ACCT. NO. 113

DATE	EXPLANATION	FO-LIO	DEBIT	CREDIT	BALANCE

Office Equipment   ACCT. NO. 134

DATE	EXPLANATION	FO-LIO	DEBIT	CREDIT	BALANCE

Notes Payable   Acct. No. 211

DATE	EXPLANATION	FO-LIO	DEBIT	CREDIT	BALANCE

Accounts Payable   Acct. No. 212

DATE	EXPLANATION	FO-LIO	DEBIT	CREDIT	BALANCE

Sales   Acct. No. 411

DATE	EXPLANATION	FO-LIO	DEBIT	CREDIT	BALANCE

Sales Returns and Allowances   Acct. No. 412

DATE	EXPLANATION	FO-LIO	DEBIT	CREDIT	BALANCE

Sales Discounts   Acct. No. 413

DATE	EXPLANATION	FO-LIO	DEBIT	CREDIT	BALANCE

Purchases   ACCT. No. 511

DATE	EXPLANATION	FO-LIO	DEBIT	CREDIT	BALANCE

Purchases Returns and Allowances   ACCT. No. 512

DATE	EXPLANATION	FO-LIO	DEBIT	CREDIT	BALANCE

Purchases Discounts   ACCT. No. 513

DATE	EXPLANATION	FO-LIO	DEBIT	CREDIT	BALANCE

Advertising Expense   ACCT. No. 615

DATE	EXPLANATION	FO-LIO	DEBIT	CREDIT	BALANCE

Sales Salaries Expense   ACCT. No. 616

DATE	EXPLANATION	FO-LIO	DEBIT	CREDIT	BALANCE

GENERAL LEDGER

Cash   ACCT. No. 111

DATE	EXPLANATION	FO-LIO	DEBIT	CREDIT	BALANCE

Accounts Receivable   ACCT. No. 113

DATE	EXPLANATION	FO-LIO	DEBIT	CREDIT	BALANCE

Office Equipment   ACCT. No. 134

DATE	EXPLANATION	FO-LIO	DEBIT	CREDIT	BALANCE

Accounts Payable   ACCT. No. 212

DATE	EXPLANATION	FO-LIO	DEBIT	CREDIT	BALANCE

Sales   ACCT. No. 411

DATE	EXPLANATION	FO-LIO	DEBIT	CREDIT	BALANCE

Sales Returns and Allowances   ACCT. No. 412

DATE	EXPLANATION	FO-LIO	DEBIT	CREDIT	BALANCE

Sales Discounts   Acct. No. 413

DATE	EXPLANATION	FO-LIO	DEBIT	CREDIT	BALANCE

Purchases   Acct. No. 511

DATE	EXPLANATION	FO-LIO	DEBIT	CREDIT	BALANCE

Purchases Returns and Allowances   Acct. No. 512

DATE	EXPLANATION	FO-LIO	DEBIT	CREDIT	BALANCE

Purchases Discounts   Acct. No. 513

DATE	EXPLANATION	FO-LIO	DEBIT	CREDIT	BALANCE

Rent Expense   Acct. No. 611

DATE	EXPLANATION	FO-LIO	DEBIT	CREDIT	BALANCE

Advertising Expense   Acct. No. 614

DATE	EXPLANATION	FO-LIO	DEBIT	CREDIT	BALANCE

ACCOUNTS RECEIVABLE LEDGER

NAME   *Ted Lee*

ADDRESS *1212 East Alder Street*

DATE	EXPLANATION	FO-LIO	DEBIT	CREDIT	BALANCE

NAME   *Gary Nash*

ADDRESS *4114 North First Avenue*

DATE	EXPLANATION	FO-LIO	DEBIT	CREDIT	BALANCE

ACCOUNTS PAYABLE LEDGER

NAME   *Best Company*

ADDRESS *Reno, Nevada*

DATE	EXPLANATION	FO-LIO	DEBIT	CREDIT	BALANCE

NAME   *Dale Company*

ADDRESS *Eastlake, Arizona*

DATE	EXPLANATION	FO-LIO	DEBIT	CREDIT	BALANCE

NAME   *Western Company*

ADDRESS   *1834 Main Street*

DATE		EXPLANATION	FO-LIO	DEBIT	CREDIT	BALANCE

PETTY CASH RECORD

DATE	EXPLANATION	RE-CEIPT NO.	RE-CEIPTS	PAY-MENTS	POST-AGE	FREIGHT-IN	MISC. GEN. EXPENSE	MISCELLANEOUS PAYMENTS	
								ACCOUNT	AMOUNT

DISTRIBUTION OF PAYMENTS

CASH DISBURSEMENTS JOURNAL

DATE	CH. NO.	PAYEE	ACCOUNT DEBITED	FO. LIO	OTHER ACCOUNTS DR.	ACCOUNTS PAYABLE DR.	PURCHASES DISCOUNTS CR.	CASH CR.

PETTY CASH RECORD

DATE	EXPLANATION	RE-CEIPT NO.	RE-CEIPTS	PAY-MENTS	DISTRIBUTION OF PAYMENTS					
					POST-AGE	FREIGHT-IN	MISC. GEN. EXPENSE	MISCELLANEOUS PAYMENTS		
								ACCOUNT	AMOUNT	

PAGE 1

CASH DISBURSEMENTS JOURNAL

DATE	CH. NO.	PAYEE	ACCOUNT DEBITED	FO. LIO	OTHER ACCOUNTS DR.	ACCOUNTS PAYABLE DR.	PURCHASES DISCOUNTS CR.	CASH CR.

PETTY CASH RECORD

DATE	EXPLANATION	RE-CEIPT NO.	RE-CEIPTS	PAY-MENTS	DISTRIBUTION OF PAYMENTS				MISCELLANEOUS PAYMENTS	
					POST-AGE	FREIGHT-IN	MISC. GEN. EXPENSE		ACCOUNT	AMOUNT

CASH DISBURSEMENTS JOURNAL

DATE	CH. NO.	PAYEE	ACCOUNT DEBITED	FO-LIO	OTHER ACCOUNTS DEBIT	CASH CREDIT

GENERAL LEDGER

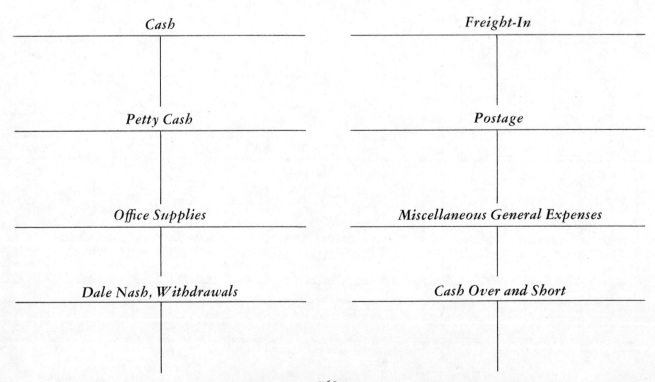

Cash	*Freight-In*
Petty Cash	*Postage*
Office Supplies	*Miscellaneous General Expenses*
Dale Nash, Withdrawals	*Cash Over and Short*

GENERAL JOURNAL

DATE	ACCOUNT TITLES AND EXPLANATION	FO-LIO	DEBIT	CREDIT

PAGE 5　　　　　　　　VOUCHER REGISTER

| | DATE | VCHR. NO. | PAYEE | WHEN AND HOW PAID | | VOUCHERS PAYABLE CREDIT | PURCHASES DEBIT | FREIGHT-IN DEBIT | |
				DATE	CH. NO.				
1									1
2									2
3									3
4									4
5									5
6									6
7									7
8									8
9									9
10									10

VOUCHER REGISTER　　　　　　　　PAGE 5

| | SALES SALARIES EXPENSE DEBIT | ADVERTISING EXPENSE DEBIT | OFFICE SALARIES EXPENSE DEBIT | OTHER ACCOUNTS DEBITED | | | |
				ACCOUNT NAME	F.	AMOUNT	
1							1
2							2
3							3
4							4
5							5
6							6
7							7
8							8
9							9
10							10

CHECK REGISTER　　　　　　　　PAGE 5

DATE	PAYEE	VCHR. NO.	CH. NO.	VOUCHERS PAYABLE DR. CASH CR.

GENERAL JOURNAL

DATE	ACCOUNT TITLES AND EXPLANATION	FO-LIO	DEBIT	CREDIT

Vouchers Payable　　　　ACCT. No. 212

DATE	EXPLANATION	FO-LIO	DEBIT	CREDIT	BALANCE

VOUCHER NUMBER	PAYEE	AMOUNT

GENERAL JOURNAL

DATE	ACCOUNT TITLES AND EXPLANATION	FO-LIO	DEBIT	CREDIT

DATE	ACCOUNT TITLES AND EXPLANATION	FO-LIO	DEBIT	CREDIT

GENERAL JOURNAL

DATE	ACCOUNT TITLES AND EXPLANATION	FO-LIO	DEBIT	CREDIT

DATE	ACCOUNT TITLES AND EXPLANATION	FO-LIO	DEBIT	CREDIT

GENERAL JOURNAL

DATE	ACCOUNT TITLES AND EXPLANATION	FO-LIO	DEBIT	CREDIT

DATE	ACCOUNT TITLES AND EXPLANATION	FO-LIO	DEBIT	CREDIT

GENERAL JOURNAL

DATE	ACCOUNT TITLES AND EXPLANATION	FO-LIO	DEBIT	CREDIT

DATE	ACCOUNT TITLES AND EXPLANATION	FO-LIO	DEBIT	CREDIT

Allowance for Doubtful Accounts   ACCT. NO. 113

DATE		EXPLANATION	FO-LIO	DEBIT	CREDIT	BALANCE
Dec.	31	Balance				1 1 5 00

Bad Debt Expense   ACCT. NO. 615

DATE		EXPLANATION	FO-LIO	DEBIT	CREDIT	BALANCE

PART 2   GENERAL JOURNAL   PAGE 1

DATE		ACCOUNT TITLES AND EXPLANATION	FO-LIO	DEBIT	CREDIT

DATE	ACCOUNT TITLES AND EXPLANATION	FO-LIO	DEBIT	CREDIT

Item_____ Location in stockroom_____

Maximum_____ Minimum_____

DATE	RECEIVED			SOLD			BALANCE		
	UNITS	COST	TOTAL	UNITS	COST	TOTAL	UNITS	COST	BALANCE

Item_____   Location in stockroom_____

Maximum _____ Minimum_____

DATE		RECEIVED			SOLD			BALANCE		
		UNITS	COST	TOTAL	UNITS	COST	TOTAL	UNITS	COST	BALANCE

DATE		ACCOUNT TITLES AND EXPLANATION	FO-LIO	DEBIT	CREDIT

MESA SALES
Comparative Income Statement, Year One

	BASED ON FIFO	BASED ON LIFO
Sales		
Cost of goods sold:		
Beginning inventory		
Purchases		
Goods for sale		
Ending inventory		
Cost of goods sold		
Gross profit on sales		

MESA SALES
Comparative Income Statement, Year Two

	BASED ON FIFO	BASED ON LIFO
Sales		
Cost of goods sold:		
Beginning inventory		
Purchases		
Goods for sale		
Ending inventory		
Cost of goods sold		
Gross profit on sales		

MESA SALES
Comparative Income Statement, Year Three

	BASED ON FIFO	BASED ON LIFO
Sales		
Cost of goods sold:		
Beginning inventory		
Purchases		
Goods for sale		
Ending inventory		
Cost of goods sold		
Gross profit on sales		

Cost of Machine		5200
Estimated salvage value		400
Total		4800

	STRAIGHT-LINE	UNITS OF PRODUCTION	DECLINING BALANCE	SUM-OF-THE-YEARS'-DIGITS
YEAR 1	1,200	880	2,600	1920
YEAR 2	1,200	1440	1,300	1440
YEAR 3	1,200	1280	650	960
YEAR 4	1,200	1200	250	480
TOTALS	4,800	4,800	4,800	4,800

GENERAL JOURNAL

DATE 1979		ACCOUNT TITLES AND EXPLANATION	FO-LIO	DEBIT	CREDIT
Jan	2	Machinery		2280	
		Cash			2280
	3	Machinery cost, Machinery		270	
		Installation cost, machinery		210	
		Cash			480
	31	Depreciation expense, Machinery		800	
		Accumulated Depr., Machinery			800
1980 July	2	Dep. Exp. Mach		400	
		Acc. Dep. Exp.		440	400

	DATE		ACCOUNT TITLES AND EXPLANATION	Fo-LIO	DEBIT	CREDIT
(A)	July	31	Cash		1600	
			~~Loss on sale of plant asset~~			
			Accumulated depreciation, machinery		1200	
			Machinery			2700
			Gain on Sale			40
(B)		2	Cash		1500	
			Loss on sale of plant asset		160	
			Accumulated depreciation, mach.		1200	
			Machinery			2700
(C)		2	Cash		1250	
			Loss from fire		310	
			Accumulated depreciation, mach.		1200	
			Machinery			2700 00

Machine Number	Amount to Be Charged to Depreciation	1978 Depreciation	1979 Depreciation	1980 Depreciation

GENERAL JOURNAL

DATE	ACCOUNT TITLES AND EXPLANATION	FO-LIO	DEBIT	CREDIT

DATE	ACCOUNT TITLES AND EXPLANATION	FO-LIO	DEBIT	CREDIT

MACHINE NUMBER	1978 DEPRECIATION	1979 DEPRECIATION	1980 DEPRECIATION	1981 DEPRECIATION	1982 DEPRECIATION
1					
2					

GENERAL JOURNAL

DATE	ACCOUNT TITLES AND EXPLANATION	FO-LIO	DEBIT	CREDIT

DATE		ACCOUNT TITLES AND EXPLANATION	FO-LIO	DEBIT	CREDIT

CHAPTER 10   PROBLEM 10-4 or 10-4A   Name

DATE	ACCOUNT TITLES AND EXPLANATION	FO-LIO	DEBIT	CREDIT

ACCT. NO. 132

DATE	EXPLANATION	FO-LIO	DEBIT	CREDIT	BALANCE

ACCT. NO. 133

DATE	EXPLANATION	FO-LIO	DEBIT	CREDIT	BALANCE

EQUIPMENT ITEM	COST	DEPRECIATION

Plant Asset
No._____

SUBSIDIARY PLANT ASSET AND DEPRECIATION RECORD

Item_____

General Ledger
Account_____

Description _____

Mfg. Serial No._____

Purchased
from _____

Where Located_____

Person Responsible for the Asset_____

Estimated Life_____   Estimated Salvage Value_____

Depreciation per year_____   per month_____

DATE	EXPLANATION	FO-LIO	ASSET RECORD			DEPRECIATION RECORD		
			DR.	CR.	BAL.	DR	CR.	BAL.

Final Disposition of the Asset_____

_____

_____

Plant Asset
No. _____

SUBSIDIARY PLANT ASSET AND DEPRECIATION RECORD

Item _____

General Ledger
Account _____

Description _____

Mfg. Serial No. _____

Purchased
from _____

Where Located _____

Person Responsible for the Asset _____

Estimated Life _____

Estimated Salvage Value _____

Depreciation per year _____

per month _____

DATE	EXPLANATION	FO-LIO	ASSET RECORD			DEPRECIATION RECORD		
			DR.	CR.	BAL.	DR	CR.	BAL.

Final Disposition of the Asset _____

_____

_____

Plant Asset
No. _____

SUBSIDIARY PLANT ASSET AND DEPRECIATION RECORD

Item_____

General Ledger
Account_____

Description_____

Mfg. Serial No._____

Purchased
from_____

Where Located_____

Person Responsible for the Asset_____

Estimated Life_____

Estimated Salvage Value_____

Depreciation per year_____

per month_____

DATE	EXPLANATION	FO-LIO	ASSET RECORD			DEPRECIATION RECORD		
			DR.	CR.	BAL.	DR	CR.	BAL.

Final Disposition of the Asset_____

_____

_____

	LAND	LAND IM-PROVEMENTS	BUILDINGS	MACHINERY

GENERAL JOURNAL

DATE		ACCOUNT TITLES AND EXPLANATION	Fo-LIO	DEBIT	CREDIT

GENERAL JOURNAL

DATE	ACCOUNT TITLES AND EXPLANATION	Fo-LIO	DEBIT	CREDIT

DATE	ACCOUNT TITLES AND EXPLANATION	FO-LIO	DEBIT	CREDIT

GENERAL JOURNAL

DATE	ACCOUNT TITLES AND EXPLANATION	Fo-LIO	DEBIT	CREDIT

DATE	ACCOUNT TITLES AND EXPLANATION	FO-LIO	DEBIT	CREDIT

Year	Beginning-of-the-Year Carrying Amount	Discount to Be Amortized Each Year	Unamortized Discount at the End of the Year	End-of-the-Year Carrying Amount
1976				
1977				
1978				
1979				

GENERAL JOURNAL

DATE	ACCOUNT TITLES AND EXPLANATION	FO-LIO	DEBIT	CREDIT

DATE	ACCOUNT TITLES AND EXPLANATION	FO-LIO	DEBIT	CREDIT

GENERAL JOURNAL

DATE	ACCOUNT TITLES AND EXPLANATION	FO-LIO	DEBIT	CREDIT

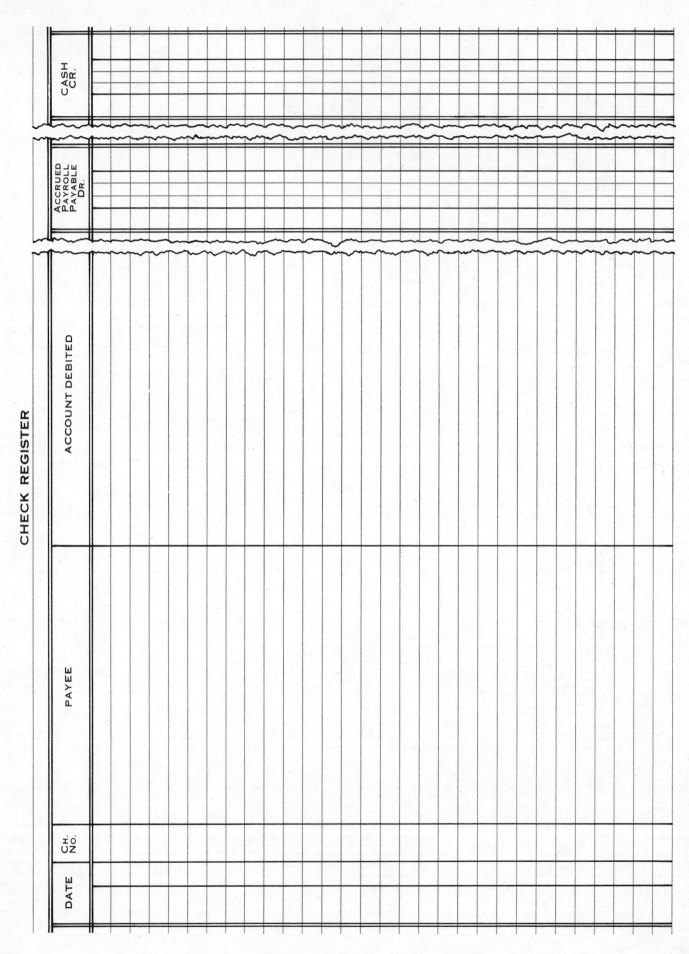

GENERAL JOURNAL

DATE	ACCOUNT TITLES AND EXPLANATION	FO-LIO	DEBIT	CREDIT

PAYROLL REGISTER

| EMPLOYEE'S NAME | CLOCK CARD NUMBER | DAILY TIME | | | | | | | TOTAL HOURS | O.T. HOURS | REG. PAY RATE | EARNINGS | | | |
		M	T	W	T	F	S	S				REGULAR PAY	O.T. PREMIUM PAY	GROSS PAY	
															1
															2
															3
															4
															5
															6
															7
															8
															9

CHECK REGISTER

DATE		CH. NO.	PAYEE	ACCOUNT DEBITED	
					1
					2
					3
					4
					5
					6
					7
					8

Week ended

	DEDUCTIONS					PAYMENT		DISTRIBUTION		
	F.I.C.A. TAXES	INCOME TAXES	MEDICAL INSURANCE	UNION DUES	TOTAL DEDUCTIONS	NET PAY	CHECK NUMBER	SALES SALARIES	OFFICE SALARIES	SHOP SALARIES
1										
2										
3										
4										
5										
6										
7										
8										
9										

	FOLIO	OTHER ACCOUNTS DR.	ACCOUNTS PAYABLE DR.	ACCRUED PAYROLL PAYABLE DR.	PURCHASES DISCOUNT CR.	CASH CR.
1						
2						
3						
4						
5						
6						
7						
8						

DATE	ACCOUNT TITLES AND EXPLANATION	FO-LIO	DEBIT	CREDIT

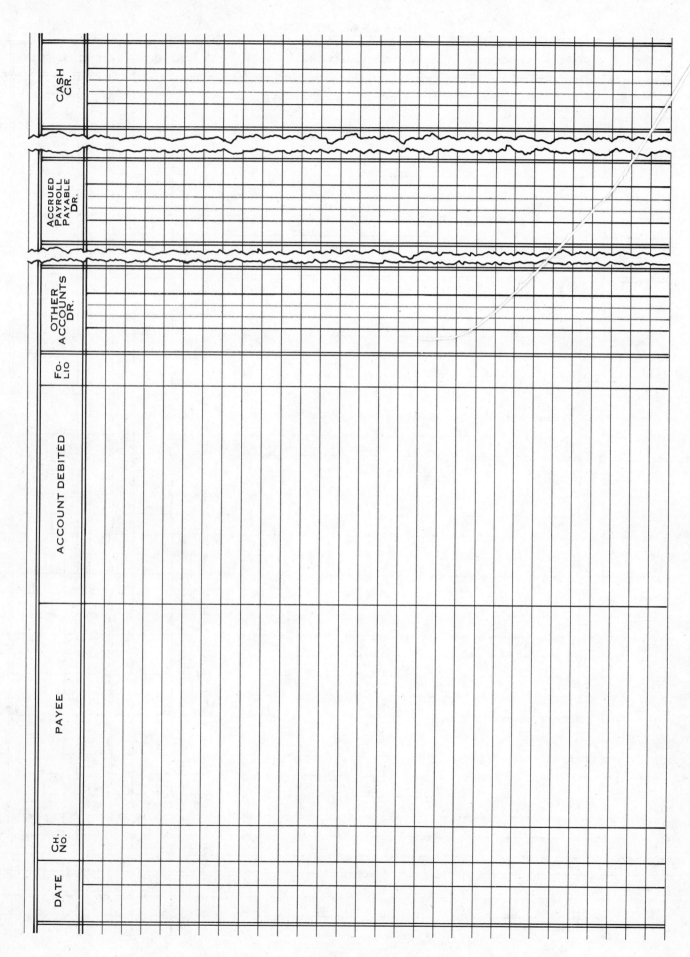

GENERAL JOURNAL

DATE	ACCOUNT TITLES AND EXPLANATION	Fo-LIO	DEBIT	CREDIT

GENERAL JOURNAL

DATE	ACCOUNT TITLES AND EXPLANATION	FO-LIO	DEBIT	CREDIT

DATE	ACCOUNT TITLES AND EXPLANATION	FO-LIO	DEBIT	CREDIT

GENERAL JOURNAL

DATE	ACCOUNT TITLES AND EXPLANATION	FO-LIO	DEBIT	CREDIT

DATE	ACCOUNT TITLES AND EXPLANATION	FO-LIO	DEBIT	CREDIT

GENERAL JOURNAL

DATE	ACCOUNT TITLES AND EXPLANATION	FO-LIO	DEBIT	CREDIT

DATE	ACCOUNT TITLES AND EXPLANATION	Fo-LIO	DEBIT	CREDIT

GENERAL JOURNAL

DATE	ACCOUNT TITLES AND EXPLANATION	FO-LIO	DEBIT	CREDIT

DATE		ACCOUNT TITLES AND EXPLANATION	FO-LIO	DEBIT	CREDIT

GENERAL JOURNAL

DATE	ACCOUNT TITLES AND EXPLANATION	FO-LIO	DEBIT	CREDIT

PLAN						
(a)						
(b)						
(c)						
(d)						

GENERAL JOURNAL

DATE	ACCOUNT TITLES AND EXPLANATION	FO-LIO	DEBIT	CREDIT

DATE	ACCOUNT TITLES AND EXPLANATION	FO-LIO	DEBIT	CREDIT

GENERAL JOURNAL

DATE	ACCOUNT TITLES AND EXPLANATION	FO-LIO	DEBIT	CREDIT

DATE	ACCOUNT TITLES AND EXPLANATION	FO-LIO	DEBIT	CREDIT

DATE	ACCOUNT TITLES AND EXPLANATION	FO-LIO	DEBIT	CREDIT

DATE		ACCOUNT TITLES AND EXPLANATION	FO-LIO	DEBIT	CREDIT

GENERAL JOURNAL

DATE	ACCOUNT TITLES AND EXPLANATION	FO-LIO	DEBIT	CREDIT

DATE	ACCOUNT TITLES AND EXPLANATION	FO-LIO	DEBIT	CREDIT

Name_____

TED'S FIXIT SHOP

Work Sheet for Year Ended December 31, 19_____

ACCOUNT TITLES	TRIAL BALANCE		ADJUSTMENTS		ADJUSTED TRIAL BALANCE		INCOME STATEMENT		BALANCE SHEET	
	DR.	CR.	DR.	CR.	DR.	CR.	DR.	CR.	DR.	CR.
Cash	975 00									
Prepaid insurance	240 00									
Repair supplies	1425 00									
Repair equipment	7215 00									
Accumulated depreciation, repair equipment		1050 00								
Accounts payable		260 00								
Ted Hall, capital		4535 00								
Ted Hall, withdrawals	8200 00									
Revenue from repairs		21135 00								
Wages expense	6860 00									
Rent expense	1800 00									
Advertising expense	265 00									
	26980 00	26980 00								

Name_____

ACCOUNT TITLES	TRIAL BALANCE		ADJUSTMENTS		ADJUSTED TRIAL BALANCE		INCOME STATEMENT		BALANCE SHEET	
	DR.	CR.	DR.	CR.	DR.	CR.	DR.	CR.	DR.	CR.

DATE	ACCOUNT TITLES AND EXPLANATION	FO-LIO	DEBIT	CREDIT

GENERAL JOURNAL

DATE	ACCOUNT TITLES AND EXPLANATION	FO-LIO	DEBIT	CREDIT

CHAPTER 4

Name_____

VILLAGE DELIVERY SERVICE

Work Sheet for Year Ended December 31, 19_____

ACCOUNT TITLES	TRIAL BALANCE		ADJUSTMENTS		ADJUSTED TRIAL BALANCE		INCOME STATEMENT		BALANCE SHEET	
	DR.	CR.	DR.	CR.	DR.	CR.	DR.	CR.	DR.	CR.
Cash	2 7 7 5 00									
Accounts receivable	4 5 5 00									
Prepaid insurance	7 2 0 00									
Office supplies	2 4 5 00									
Office equipment	2 4 6 0 00									
Accumulated depreciation, office equipment		4 7 0 00								
Delivery equipment	1 0 7 9 0 00									
Accumulated depreciation, delivery equipment		3 1 5 0 00								
Accounts payable		2 9 0 00								
Unearned delivery service revenue		4 5 0 00								
Betty Lee, capital		9 8 5 5 00								
Betty Lee, withdrawals	1 0 4 0 0 00									
Delivery service revenue		3 8 9 3 5 00								
Office rent expense	6 0 0 00									
Telephone expense	2 4 5 00									
Office salaries expense	5 0 6 0 00									
Truck drivers' wages	1 6 3 2 0 00									
Gas, oil, and repairs	2 1 8 0 00									
Garage rent expense	9 0 0 00									
	5 3 1 5 0 00	5 3 1 5 0 00								

ACCOUNT TITLES	TRIAL BALANCE		ADJUSTMENTS		ADJUSTED TRIAL BALANCE		INCOME STATEMENT		BALANCE SHEET	
	DR.	CR.	DR.	CR.	DR.	CR.	DR.	CR.	DR.	CR.
Cash										
Merchandise inventory										
Store supplies										
Prepaid insurance										
Store equipment										
Accumulated depreciation, store equipment										
Accounts payable										
Lee Davis, capital										
Lee Davis, withdrawals										
Sales										
Sales returns and allowances										
Sales discounts										
Purchases										
Purchases returns and allowances										
Purchases discounts										
Freight-in										
Sales salaries expense										
Rent expense										
Advertising expense										
Utilities expense										

COMBINED CASH JOURNAL

CASH		SALES DISCOUNTS	PURCHASES DISCOUNTS	DATE	CHECK No.	ACCOUNT TITLES AND EXPLANATIONS	FOLIO	OTHER GENERAL LEDGER ACCOUNTS		ACCOUNTS RECEIVABLE		ACCOUNTS PAYABLE		PURCHASES	SALES	INV. No.
DEBIT	CREDIT	DEBIT	CREDIT					DEBIT	CREDIT	DEBIT	CREDIT	DEBIT	CREDIT	DEBIT	CREDIT	

Extra Worksheet Form

ACCOUNT TITLES	TRIAL BALANCE		ADJUSTMENTS		ADJUSTED TRIAL BALANCE		INCOME STATEMENT		BALANCE SHEET	
	DR.	CR.	DR.	CR.	DR.	CR.	DR.	CR.	DR.	CR.

Extra Work Sheet Form

ACCOUNT TITLES	TRIAL BALANCE		ADJUSTMENTS		ADJUSTED TRIAL BALANCE		INCOME STATEMENT		BALANCE SHEET	
	DR.	CR.	DR.	CR.	DR.	CR.	DR.	CR.	DR.	CR.

32-0570-08

ISBN 0-256-01995-9